Svetlana Chmakova's Nightschool

The Weirn Books

VOLUME ONE

D1535574

Yen
Press

WE PUSH DARKNESS
AWAY...

...WITH OUR FIRES
AND LAMPS AND
BRIGHTLY LIT CITIES.

BUT EVEN
THERE,
SHADOWS
LURK.

IN THE DARK
CORNERS, BEHIND
THE COLD GLASS
OF DARKENED
MIRRORS.

AS OLD AS OUR
WORLD IS THIS
ONE—THE WORLD
OF NIGHT. THE
PLACE OF BLOOD
MAGIC, SWIFT
WINGS, AND
SHARP TEETH
BARED IN A
KNOWING SMILE.

PUSH IT AWAY
THOUGH WE MAY
IN OUR CITIES...

...IT'S STILL THERE.

Dedicated to my parents

and

Barry McCarthy

Thank you ♡

CONTENTS

PEEK

ARGH, DON'T GO IN THERE!!

HEY, THE LIGHT SWITCH DOESN'T WORK.

WELL, IT'S PRETTY DARK, BUT OTHER THAN THAT...

THIS ONE'S BEEN CLOSED SINCE LAST *YEAR*. AND TELL ME IT DOESN'T GIVE YOU THE CREEPS!

WOW, THIS MIRROR'S HUGE.

9

GOOD EVENING, HOW ARE—

MADAM NIGHT PRINCIPAL, I WOULD LIKE TO LODGE A FORMAL COMPLAINT!!

...O-OH. MY FAVORITE WAY TO START WORK...

WE ABSOLUTELY MUST MOVE THE GATE TO A BETTER LOCATION!!

YOU JUST NARROWLY MISSED MEETING THREE VERY SUSPICIOUS DAY STUDENTS FACE-TO-FACE!

...OH DEAR, UM... ...CAN I HAVE MY COFFEE FIRST?

SNAP

I AM UNDERMINED AT EVERY TURN!

I CANNOT WORK IN THESE CONDITIONS!!

SLINK SLINK

...I'LL JUST HAVE MY COFFEE FIRST.

AND THE NEW NIGHT KEEPER IS STILL NOT HERE!

....! SHE'S NOT? DOESN'T SHE HAVE ANOTHER TRAINING SESSION WITH YOU TODAY?

YES!

SHE IS ALWAYS LATE!!

15

FIRE HER ALREADY.

BUT THE KIDS LOVE HER...

LET'S GIVE HER ANOTHER CHANCE! I AM SURE SHE'S JUST ON HER WAY...

ELSEWHERE IN THE CITY.

GUESS WHO!

H_2O

PLOOSH

AAAAAAH!!

19

NO.

MAYBE WITH OTHER PEOPLE...

I, UM...
I-I THINK YOU COULD WORK AROUND THAT. IT'S BEEN WHAT, THREE YEARS? I MEAN, YOU'RE DOING ALL RIGHT WITH ME.

─:SIGH:─ FINE. STUDY PAGES 29-54. TRY NOT TO BURN THE HOUSE DOWN.

I HAVE A BUCKET OF WATER, JUST IN CASE. YOU MAY REMEMBER ITS COUSIN FROM FIFTEEN MINUTES AGO.

HEH

SEE YOU IN THE MORNING!

I KNOW.

I LOVE YOU TOO.

NUZZLE

CASSIDY.

SIR?

YOU AND TERESA ARE IN CHARGE TONIGHT. BRING EVERYONE BACK SAFE.

YES, SIR.

CURFEW'S AT 6 A.M. YOU KNOW WHAT HAPPENS FOR MISSING IT.

SEAL.

KCHK

THERE... FINALLY.

DO YOU HAVE ALL THE...

...KEYS.

HOWLL

SSHAAAA

SCREEECH

...A BIT EARLY FOR STUDENTS TO BE ARRIVING.

OH! THAT'S MY MANGA/ANIME CLUB.

...

...YOUR WHAT?

A M-MANGA CLUB...

A-AND ANIME...UM, CARTOONS...

...

...YOU STARTED AN EXTRA-CURRICULAR ACTIVITIES CLUB?

UM, KIND OF...

SEVERAL...

WE DON'T HAVE A BUDGET, I KNOW, BUT WE CAN FUND-RAISE...

SCRBL

GIVE THIS TO MADAM CHEN. IT'S A RECOMMENDATION THAT YOU GET AN ACTIVITIES BUDGET AND A RAISE.

...

OH PLEASE DON'T FIRE ME, I NEED THIS JOB! ;___;

...

THANK YOU THANK YOU THANK YOU!!

IF YOU ARE THANKFUL, STOP BEING LATE TO WORK!!

AND WE ARE NOT ON HUGGING TERMS, SO GET OFF!

IF I CAN DO IT, SO CAN YOU!! BEING A KEEPER IS NOT SUP-POSED TO BE EASY!

BUT IT'S SO HARD TO WAKE UP...

I AM LATE FOR DINNER, MISS TREVENEY, I HAVE TO GO.

KEEP UP THE GOOD WORK.

SHAKE
SHAKE

TIME
TO GO.

SNAG

TUG
TUG

AND SINCE
YOU'RE WITH
ME, YOU'LL
PROTECT ME!
SO THERE'S
NO PROBLEM,
RIGHT?

...

...LOOK,
WHEN SARAH
SAYS "DON'T
LEAVE THE
HOUSE"...

...WHAT SHE
ACTUALLY MEANS
IS "DON'T LEAVE
THE HOUSE
UNPROTECTED."

SO, AS IT CLEARLY STATES IN THE NIGHT STUDENT GUIDEBOOK...

...CASTING SPELLS OUTSIDE THE CLASSROOM ON SCHOOL GROUNDS IS *FORBIDDEN*.

BREAKING THIS RULE TRIGGERS A SPECIAL WARD THAT *MARKS* THE CASTER...

...LIKE SO.

IT WAS AN ACCIDENT, I SWEAR!

THAT'S WHAT THEY ALWAYS SAY. EXCUSE #1 IN THE NIGHT TEACHER'S HANDBOOK.

THERE IS A TOP FIFTY LIST, SEE?

OHHHH!

TMP

TMP TMP

TMP

...

NO TRESPASSING

AWW, THEY FIXED THE HOLE!

HMM

...!

WHAT WAS THAT?

I'M OKAY, I'M OKAY.

...WHAT WAS I SAYING?

?

WELL, WHATEVER, LET'S GO.

...SHEESH, CAN I HAVE MORE WEIRD TONIGHT, PLEASE?

DRAG DRAG

≈GRUMBLE≈ HOPE NO ONE GOT BURIED ON MY PRACTICE SITE. ≈GRUMBLE≈

GIRL, YOU STILL HERE? SCOOT ON HOME BEFORE YOU'RE SOMEONE'S *DINNER.*

WHAT'S YOUR PROBLEM?!

...MY PROBLEM?

I...I KNOW WHO YOU ARE!

BIG FRIGGING DEAL! BEING THE LAW DOESN'T GIVE YOU THE EXCUSE TO BE A BITCH!

WHAT DID YOU JUST CALL ME...?

I-I... WELL...

•••

83

CRUSH

GET THE
OTHER
HAND.

YANK

○ ○ ○

Chapter 4

...J'S A LIGHT-WEIGHT, OKAY.

BUT WHATEVER THAT THING WAS, IT TOOK OUT *TERRANCE.*

AND NOH.

WITHOUT EVEN A FIGHT.

THIS IS OUT OF OUR LEAGUE. WE HAVE TO TELL THE OLD MAN.

...

...I CAN'T
REMEMBER.

FOUR
HUNTERS,
I *SAW*
THEM.

DID THEY
SEE ME...?

NO, NO. I
WAS HIDDEN.
AND FAR.

AND THEY
WERE BUSY
WITH THE
VAMPIRE
MISSING LINK
AND HIS
GIRLFRIENDS.

I GRABBED
MY BAG,
RAN,
AND...

AND
THEN
WHAT?

118

I CAN'T TELL SARAH, ARE YOU KIDDING?!

SHE'LL GROUND ME FOR LIFE!!

...HOW MANY COOKIES TO KEEP YOU QUIET?

!!

DEAL.

I MIGHT AS WELL MAKE A NEW BATCH. COULD USE SOME TOO...

CAN'T BELIEVE I ALMOST RAN INTO HUNTERS FACE-TO-FACE, URGH.

?

TUG

OH GOOD...

I'D HATE TO FIRE YOU, YOU'VE BEEN EVER SO WONDERFUL HERE. U.U

YOU'VE DONE IMPRESSIVE WORK IN YOUR SHORT TIME HERE.

SO, I MUST SAY I AGREE WITH MRS. HATCHER'S NOTE WHOLE-HEARTEDLY!

RAISE $?

RAISE $?

...I CAN'T GIVE YOU A RAISE.

I CAN, HOWEVER, SEE ABOUT THE CLUB BUDGETS!

EXACTLY HOW MANY HAVE YOU, ERM, STARTED, LET'S SEE...

ANIM/ MEHNGA?

ANIME MANGA.

I SEE, I SEE.

A WRITER'S GROUP, A MIDNIGHT NEWS DAILY—OH, A STUDENT NEWS-LETTER, THAT SHOULD BE FUN!

...!

A "VAM-PIRES SUCK" CLUB...?

THAT ONE WASN'T MY IDEA, IT WAS LARS!!

I-IT'S TO HELP PROMOTE A POSITIVE COUNTER TO THE NEGATIVE STEREOTYPE OF VAMPIRES IN OUR SOCIETY.

OH, LARS IS THE LAST PERSON WHO SHOULD BE DOING THAT.

I WILL NEED TO HAVE A TALK WITH THAT MAN.

OH! DO YOU MIND HAVING ONE WITH MR. ROI, AS WELL...?

UH-OH, WHAT'S HE DONE NOW?

H-HIS... HIS CLASS PRESENTATIONS...

RRUMBLE

.....!!

RESTORE.

FWIP

TO WHAT DO I OWE THE PLEASURE?

AW CRAP, I DIDN'T GET THAT LAST PATTERN...DO YOU HAVE IT?

U-UH. UMM. DO YOU...I HAVE...

...A MESSAGE! FROM MADAME CHEN!

...A RENTED PROPERTY...

...NOT PERSONAL LAB...

...SMITH-EREENS...

ONE: IF MADAME CHEN HAS SOMETHING TO SAY TO ME, I ENCOURAGE PERSONAL CONTACT IN THE FUTURE.

...PLEASE?

TWO: THESE PREMISES ARE INADEQUATE FOR MY LECTURES. AS LONG AS I AM TO SUFFER THESE ILL TEACHING ACCOMMODATIONS...

...THE ILL TEACHING ACCOMODATIONS ARE TO SUFFER *ME.*

GOOD NIGHT.

133

...YOU KNOW, IT REALLY CAN GET STUCK THAT WAY.

PLEASE STOP WRECKING THE SCHOOL, THANK YOOOOOUUUUUU!!!!

DASH!

HM.

SEVERAL MORE SMALL DISASTERS LATER...

UGH, ALL THE CRAZY IS LOOSE TONIGHT.

WAS LITERALLY PUTTING OUT FIRES.

PAT PAT

PLOP

SHFL

o o o

MOMENT OF PEACE

RUSTLE

Chapter 5

FU FU FU

DRAWN PORTRAITS.

THE ART CLUB VOLUNTEERED THEIR BEST ARTISTS FOR THIS. I ALREADY TALKED TO THEM.

...THIS...

HE'S CUTTING SCHOOL TONIGHT.

HA-HA, IT TOTALLY IS! THE ATTITUDE IS DEAD ON.

...HEEEY, IS THAT NICHOLAS?!

...

AND IF THEY DON'T LIKE THE DRAWINGS?

THEY HAVE THE OPTION OF PROVIDING THEIR OWN!

...

...CLUBS WORKING TOGETHER, VAMPIRES GETTING SOCIALLY INVOLVED, FOR ONCE— THIS IS CLEVER ON SO MANY LEVELS. THERE IS NO WAY SHE WILL SAY NO.

...RONEE!

?

I-IF, IF I GET YOU THE YEARBOOK, CAN YOU DO SOMETHING ABOUT MR. ROI TOO? :D;;;

...

NO. MR. ROI DOES NOT OBEY ANY KNOWN LAWS OF OUR UNIVERSE.

AWWW. DANGIT.

IT'S TRUE...

HE LOOKS HOT DOING IT TOO.

HEY, WATCH IT.

...

Y-YES. SOFTIE, THAT'S ME. ER...

Well, no worries, I think we still have some Snakol.

...WE DO?!

Yeah, on top of the shelf to your right, I think?

Just give her a couple of spoons, she'll be all right.

Oh, I think someone's at the door. Gotta go! See you in the morning.

SEE YA!

BLINK

Snakol*

INGREDIENTS:
- dried newt eyeballs
- beetle-juice
- vegetables
- snake oil
- really foul-tasting mushrooms

* MAY CONTAIN PEANUTS

150

MMMMM, DELICIOUS!

!!

DASH!

...HEY, COME BACK HERE!

OH, HELLO!

ARE YOU LOST?

DID YOU NEED SOMETHING?

...IN THE WEST WING...?

LET'S CHECK IT OUT.

151

OH, THIS HALLWAY ISN'T EVEN IN USE TONIGHT... THIS DEFINITELY SHOULDN'T BE HERE.

WAIT HERE. I'LL CHECK IT OUT AND BE RIGHT BACK, OKAY?

NOD

HELLO?

IS THERE SOMEONE HERE?

YOU HAVE TO KEEP YOUR PRESENTATIONS TO THE EAST WING TONIGHT, PLEASE!

HEL-LOOOOO!

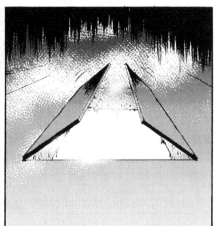

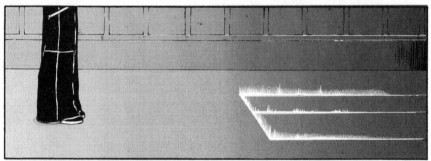
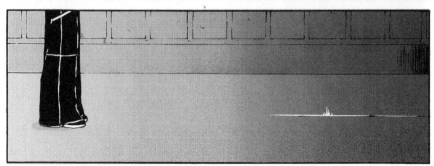

IT'S
DONE.

FU
FU
FU

YES, WE DID! SHE'S NEW, BUT SHE'S A GEM.

Oh? What's the name?

IT'S ...

....?

UH. WE...

...WE DON'T *HAVE* A NEW NIGHT KEEPER.

WHY DID I SAY WE...?

Well, I have a recommendation. I'll send it over.

BLINK

This meeting is adjourned. Back into the breach, guys!

ER. YES. THANK YOU.

. . .

157

SHELLY, DO WE HAVE A NIGHT KEEPER?

NOT SINCE YOU FIRED THE LAST ONE A MONTH AGO. REALLY NEED ONE, THOUGH.

I WAS SO *SURE.* HM.

HUH.

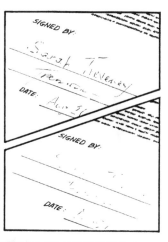

SIGNED BY:
Sarah Teverey

DATE: Aug 5

SIGNED BY:

DATE:

WELL, THERE IS DEFINITELY A CONTRACT... IT MUST HAVE A NAME.

FLIP FLIP

IT'S BLANK?
...

...
WHY WAS I LOOKING AT THIS AGAIN?

NO MORE
COOKIES FOR
YOU, EVER,
EVER, *EVER*...

GRUMBLE
GRUMBLE

GRUMBLE
GRUMBLE

CLEAN

CLEAN

CLEAN

PHEW.

...PROBABLY *TOO* CLEAN. SARAH WILL JUST MESS IT UP AGAIN.

TAK

HM.

Chapter 6

SNK

PASSAGE.

...BUT NOT TO THIS ONE.

SHE STILL HAS A REFLECTION. IS MONA AROUND TODAY?

GO. I WILL LOOK AFTER HER.

THANK YOU, TAKER.

WH-WHAT...

IT'S ALL RIGHT, THIS IS A FRIEND. GO WITH HER, SHE'LL TELL YOU WHAT YOU NEED TO KNOW.

GOOD LUCK. STAY AWAY FROM BAD PLACES.

...

I DO NOT RECOGNIZE THIS CONDITION.

WHO WAS THE ATTACKER?

WE... DON'T KNOW.

CAN'T YOU DO SOMETHING?

THEY ARE NOT FEELING ANYTHING, IN FACT. THEY ARE NOT DEAD...BUT THEY ARE NOT ALIVE, EITHER. THEY...

THERE IS NOTHING I CAN TAKE HERE.

NO SPELLS, NO INJURIES. THEY ARE FEELING NO PAIN.

TURN

TEACHER!

HOW...?

PEEK

BOW

MAR!! ARE YOU BACK?

NOD

EXPLAIN.

177

...WHAT IS THIS?

I *JUST* TALKED TO HER.

...THE SCHOOL.

. . .

WHOSE DECISION WAS IT TO RETREAT INSTEAD OF HUNT?

. . .

...MINE, SIR.

TERESA?

I WANTED TO HUNT.

ннин

NOD

NNGH

HHUH

HHUH

STEADY. DEEP BREATHS.

...LAYING SPELLTRAPS IS ILLEGAL NOW!!

YES. FOR ALL *THAT'S* WORTH TO THE NIGHT.

...THE LIGHTS AREN'T ON?

SCHOOL SHOULD STILL BE IN SESSION, IT'S BARELY MIDNIGHT...

HELLO?

TO BE CONTINUED IN NIGHTSCHOOL VOL. 2...
LOOK FOR NIGHTSCHOOL EVERY MONTH IN YEN

END OF VOLUME 1!

HI, AND THANK YOU FOR READING!! I HOPE YOU ENJOYED THIS BOOK! YOU KNOW, I HAD TO TRAVEL A LOT THIS YEAR FOR WORK, SO THIS VOLUME IS A BIT OF A GLOBETROTTER... HERE ARE SOME OF THE PLACES WHERE I DREW THIS:

...ON A KITCHEN TABLE IN MONTREAL, CANADA!

SO TIRED...

ZZZz

...ON MY KNEE IN PARIS, FRANCE!

LE AIRPORT

(...I WAS TOLD THAT WHEN I SPEAK FRENCH, I SOUND LIKE A BOND GIRL?)

BONJOUR, JE VOUDRAIS UN JUS D'ORANGE ♥

TOY

...ON A COFFEE TABLE IN ENGLAND (AT EMMA VIECELI'S HOUSE, YAY ART CAMP!)

PRR PRR ♥

TEA! ↓

EMMA'S CAT WAS VERY FRIENDLY

...AND SOMETIMES EVEN IN MY OWN STUDIO BACK AT HOME!!

...THIS FEELS SO WEIRD...

AND NOW, AS PER USUAL, IT'S TIME TO MEET THE CAST! AND SEEING AS THE MAIN CHARACTER'S A LITTLE TIED UP...

I HATE YOU

...LET'S CHECK ON THE REST OF THE CREW!

WOOOO NEAH!

HAHA! I LOVE KARAOKE

POKE

SODA

...

OUT CELEBRATING (YOU'RE NOT INVITED, DON'T CALL ♥)

...

...HEY, I JUST FIGURED OUT WHAT HAPPENS IN THE NEXT VOLUME... EVERYONE ACCIDENTALLY GETS RUN OVER BY A TRUCK.

~THANQ's~

 Barry McCarthy -- my high school art teacher. Thank you, Mr. McCarthy, for showing me that I could be an artist and for letting me draw cartoons. (And for making me draw stuff other than cartoons... You were right, it was important :D;;;)

 My family and friends -- for being the rocking foundation of the whirlwind that is my life, I couldn't do this half as well without you.

(...Especially without Dee, my long-suffering tone artist with a hunted look in her eyes, and Sasha, my invaluable little sister and life-saver <3)

Yen Press crew ♥ -- this book would not be the same elsewhere. Thank you for helping me run amok on the pages of Yen Plus!!

(...Especially to my editor JuYoun, for guiding me through this very different writing process and for putting up with my loose grasp on the concept of "deadline"... Yes, Lillian, I see you smiling there!! Also, huge thanks to Kurt, for supporting my work all these years and for the encouragement at a time when I really needed it. Thank you, sir!)

 Judy! -- my wonderful agent. Thank you for always looking out for me! *HUGS*

Dave and Raina -- those reference pictures helped So Much, I can't even say. Yay!!

Everyone who read this book! --you, dear readers, are a huge reason for why I am able to do this. Thank you so much for reading, for writing wonderful letters and for sending such amazing art.
I LOVE YOU!!

Jan. 12, 2009
(hope I didn't forget anyone!!)
Svetlana

SEE YOU NEXT TIME!

WHERE ARE MY PAGES!..

EDITOR'S OFFICE

"TEN" WUZ HERE

ALEX WUZ HERE

VAMPIRES ♥ (R) PEEPLE 2

BUSY POSING FOR AUTHOR PICTURE

NIGHTSCHOOL
THE WEIRN BOOKS ①

SVETLANA CHMAKOVA

Toning Artist: Dee DuPuy

Lettering: JuYoun Lee

NIGHTSCHOOL: The Weirn Books, Vol. 1 © 2009 Svetlana Chmakova.

Yen Press
Hachette Book Group
237 Park Avenue, New York, NY 10017

Visit our Web sites at www.HachetteBookGroup.com
and www.YenPress.com.

Yen Press is an imprint of Hachette Book Group, Inc. The Yen Press name and logo are trademarks of Hachette Book Group, Inc.

First Yen Press Edition: April 2009

ISBN: 978-0-7595-2859-8

10 9 8 7 6 5 4 3 2 1

BVG

Printed in the United States of America